Tasty Sirtfood Diet Recipes for Weight Loss – 2 Book in 1

More than 100 Tasty Recipes to Lose Weight for Good and Activate Your Skinny Gene

By

Lara Middleton

Sirt Diet Recipes for Breakfast

by

Lara Middleton

Additionally, the information in the following pages is intended only for informational purposes and should thus be thought of as universal. As befitting its nature, it is presented without assurance regarding its prolonged validity or interim quality. Trademarks that are mentioned are done without written consent and can in no way be considered an endorsement from the trademark holder.

Table of Contents

Matcha Green Juice

Preparation time: 10 minutes

Cooking time: 0 minutes

Servings: 2

Ingredients:

- 5 ounces fresh kale

- 2 ounces fresh arugula

- ¼ cup fresh parsley

- 4 celery stalks

- 1 green apple, cored and chopped

- 1 (1-inch) piece fresh ginger, peeled

- 1 lemon, peeled

- ½ teaspoon matcha green tea

Directions:

- Add all ingredients into a juicer and extract the juice according to the manufacturer's method.

- Pour into 2 glasses and serve immediately.

Nutrition:

- Calories: 113

- Fat: 0.6 g

- Carbohydrates: 26.71 g

- Protein: 3.8 g

Celery Juice

Preparation time: 10 minutes

Cooking time: 0 minutes

Servings: 2

Ingredients:

- 8 celery stalks with leaves

- 2 tablespoons fresh ginger, peeled

- 1 lemon, peeled

- ½ cup filtered water

- Pinch of salt

Directions:

- Place all the ingredients in a blender and pulse until well combined.

- Through a fine mesh strainer, strain the juice and transfer into 2 glasses.

- Serve immediately.

Nutrition:

- Calories: 32

- Fat: 0.5 g

- Carbohydrates: 6.5 g

- Protein: 1 g

Kale & Orange Juice

Preparation time: 10 minutes

Cooking time: 0 minutes

Servings: 2

Ingredients:

- 5 large oranges, peeled and sectioned

- 2 bunches fresh kale

Directions:

- Add all ingredients into a juicer and extract the juice according to the manufacturer's method.

- Pour into 2 glasses and serve immediately.

Nutrition:

- Calories: 315

- Fat: 0.6 g

- Carbohydrates: 75.1 g

- Protein: 10.3 g

Apple & Cucumber Juice

Preparation time: 10 minutes

Cooking time: 0 minutes

Servings: 2

Ingredients:

- 3 large apples, cored and sliced

- 2 large cucumbers, sliced

- 4 celery stalks

- 1 (1-inch) piece fresh ginger, peeled

- 1 lemon, peeled

Directions:

- Add all ingredients into a juicer and extract the juice according to the manufacturer's method.

- Pour into 2 glasses and serve immediately.

Nutrition:

- Calories: 230

- Fat: 1.1 g

- Carbohydrates: 59.5 g

- Protein: 3.3 g

1

2

Lemony Green Juice

Preparation time: 10 minutes

Cooking time: 0 minutes

Servings: 2

Ingredients:

- 2 large green apples, cored and sliced

- 4 cups fresh kale leaves

- 4 tablespoons fresh parsley leaves

- 1 tablespoon fresh ginger, peeled

- 1 lemon, peeled

- ½ cup filtered water

- Pinch of salt

Directions:

- Place all the ingredients in a blender and pulse until well combined.

- Through a fine mesh strainer, strain the juice and transfer into 2 glasses.

- Serve immediately.

Nutrition:

- Calories: 196

- Fat: 0.6 g

- Carbohydrates: 47.9 g

- Protein: 5.2 g

Kale Scramble

Preparation time: 10 minutes

Cooking time: 6 minutes

Servings: 2

Ingredients:

- 4 eggs

- 1/8 teaspoon ground turmeric

- Salt and ground black pepper, to taste

- 1 tablespoon water

- 2 teaspoons olive oil

- 1 cup fresh kale, tough ribs removed and chopped

Directions:

- In a bowl, add the eggs, turmeric, salt, black pepper, and water and with a whisk, beat until foamy.

- In a wok, heat the oil over medium heat.

- Add the egg mixture and stir to combine.

- Immediately, reduce the heat to medium-low and cook for about 1–2 minutes, stirring frequently.

- Stir in the kale and cook for about 3–4 minutes, stirring frequently.

- Remove from the heat and serve immediately.

Nutrition:

- Calories: 183

- Fat: 13.4 g

- Carbohydrates: 4.3 g

- Protein: 12.1 g

Buckwheat Porridge

Preparation time: 10 minutes

Cooking time: 15 minutes

Servings: 2

Ingredients:

- 1 cup buckwheat, rinsed

- 1 cup unsweetened almond milk

- 1 cup water

- ½ teaspoon ground cinnamon

- ½ teaspoon vanilla extract

- 1–2 tablespoons raw honey

- ¼ cup fresh blueberries

Directions:

- In a pan, add all the ingredients (except honey and blueberries) over medium-high heat and bring to a boil.

- Now, reduce the heat to low and simmer, covered for about 10 minutes.

- Stir in the honey and remove from the heat.

- Set aside, covered, for about 5 minutes.

- With a fork, fluff the mixture, and transfer into serving bowls.

- Top with blueberries and serve.

Nutrition:

- Calories: 358

- Fat: 4.7 g

- Carbohydrates: 3.7 g

- Protein: 12 g

Blueberry Muffins

Preparation time: 15 minutes

Cooking time: 20 minutes

Servings: 8

Ingredients

- 1 cup buckwheat flour

- ¼ cup arrowroot starch

- 1½ teaspoons baking powder

- ¼ teaspoon sea salt

- 2 eggs

- ½ cup unsweetened almond milk

- 2–3 tablespoons maple syrup

- 2 tablespoons coconut oil, melted

- 1 cup fresh blueberries

Directions:

- Preheat your oven to 350°F and line 8 cups of a muffin tin.

- In a bowl, place the buckwheat flour, arrowroot starch, baking powder, and salt, and mix well.

- In a separate bowl, place the eggs, almond milk, maple syrup, and coconut oil, and beat until well combined.

- Now, place the flour mixture and mix until just combined.

- Gently, fold in the blueberries.

- Transfer the mixture into prepared muffin cups evenly.

- Bake for about 25 minutes or until a toothpick inserted in the center comes out clean.

- Remove the muffin tin from oven and place onto a wire rack to cool for about 10 minutes.

- Carefully invert the muffins onto the wire rack to cool completely before serving.

Nutrition:

- Calories: 136

- Fat: 5.3 g

- Carbohydrates: 20.7 g

- Protein: 3.5 g

Chocolate Waffles

Preparation time: 15 minutes

Cooking time: 24 minutes

Servings: 8

Ingredients

- 2 cups unsweetened almond milk

- 1 tablespoon fresh lemon juice

- 1 cup buckwheat flour

- ½ cup cacao powder

- ¼ cup flaxseed meal

- 1 teaspoon baking soda

- 1 teaspoon baking powder

- ¼ teaspoons kosher salt

- 2 large eggs

- ½ cup coconut oil, melted

- ¼ cup dark brown sugar

- 2 teaspoons vanilla extract

- 2 ounces unsweetened dark chocolate, chopped roughly

Directions:

- In a bowl, add the almond milk and lemon juice and mix well.

- Set aside for about 10 minutes.

- In a bowl, place buckwheat flour, cacao powder, flaxseed meal, baking soda, baking powder, and salt, and mix well.

- In the bowl of almond milk mixture, place the eggs, coconut oil, brown sugar, and vanilla extract, and beat until smooth.

- Now, place the flour mixture and beat until smooth.

- Gently, fold in the chocolate pieces.

- Preheat the waffle iron and then grease it.

- Place the desired amount of the mixture into the preheated waffle iron and cook for about 3 minutes, or until golden-brown.

- Repeat with the remaining mixture.

Nutrition:

- Calories: 295

- Fat: 22.1 g

- Carbohydrates: 1.5 g

- Protein: 6.3 g

3

Moroccan Spiced Eggs

Preparation time: 1 hour

Cooking time: 50 minutes

Servings: 2

Ingredients:

- 1 tsp. olive oil

- 1 shallot, stripped and finely hacked

- 1 red (chime) pepper, deseeded and finely hacked

- 1 garlic clove, stripped and finely hacked

- 1 courgette (zucchini), stripped and finely hacked

- 1 tbsp. tomato purees (glue)

- ½ tsp. gentle stew powder

- ¼ tsp. ground cinnamon

- ¼ tsp. ground cumin

- ½ tsp. salt

- 1 × 400g (14oz) can hack tomatoes

- 1 x 400g (14oz) may chickpeas in water

- A little bunch of level leaf parsley (10g (1/3oz)), cleaved

- Four medium eggs at room temperature

Directions:

- Heat the oil in a pan; include the shallot and red (ringer) pepper and fry delicately for 5 minutes. At that point include the garlic and courgette (zucchini) and cook for one more

39

moment or two. Include the tomato puree (glue), flavour and salt and mix through.

- Add the cleaved tomatoes and chickpeas (dousing alcohol and all) and increment the warmth to medium. With the top of the dish, stew the sauce for 30 minutes – ensure it is delicately rising all through and permit it to lessen in volume by around 33%.

- Remove from the warmth and mix in the cleaved parsley.

- Preheat the grill to 200C/180C fan/350F.

- When you are prepared to cook the eggs, bring the tomato sauce up to a delicate stew and move to a little broiler confirmation dish.

- Crack the eggs on the dish and lower them delicately into the stew. Spread with thwart and prepare in the grill for 10-15 minutes. Serve the blend in unique dishes with the eggs coasting on the top.

Nutrition:

- Calories: 116 kcal

- Protein: 6.97 g

- Fat: 5.22 g

- Carbohydrates: 13.14 g

Chilaquiles with Gochujang

Preparation time: 30 minutes

Cooking time: 20 minutes

Servings: 2

Ingredients:

- 1 dried ancho Chile

- 2 cups of water

- 1 cup squashed tomatoes

- 2 cloves of garlic

42

- 1 teaspoon genuine salt

- 1/2 tablespoons Gochujang

- 5 to 6 cups tortilla chips

- 3 enormous eggs

- 1 tablespoon olive oil

Directions:

- Get the water to heat a pot. I cheated marginally and heated the water in an electric pot and emptied it into the pan.

- Add the anchor Chile to the bubbled water and drench for 15 minutes to give it an opportunity to stout up.

- When completed, use tongs or a spoon to extricate Chili. Make sure to spare the water for the sauce.

- Mix the doused Chili, 1 cup of saved high temp water, squashed tomatoes, garlic, salt and gochujang.

- Empty sauce into a large dish and heat 4 to 5 minutes. Heat and include the tortilla chips.

- Mix the chips to cover with the sauce. In a different skillet, shower a teaspoon of oil and fry an egg on top, until the whites have settled.

- Plate the egg and cook the remainder of the eggs. Sear the eggs while you heat the red sauce.

- Top the chips with the seared eggs, cotija, hacked cilantro, jalapeños, onions and avocado. Serve right away.

Nutrition:

- Calories: 484 kcal

- Protein: 14.55 g

- Fat: 18.62 g

- Carbohydrates: 64.04 g

Twice Baked Breakfast Potatoes

Preparation time: 1 hour 10 minutes

Cooking time: 1 hour

Servings: 2

Ingredients:

- 2 medium reddish brown potatoes, cleaned and pricked with a fork everywhere

- 2 tablespoons unsalted spread

- 3 tablespoons overwhelming cream

- 4 rashers cooked bacon

- 4 huge eggs

- ½ cup destroyed cheddar

- Daintily cut chives

- Salt and pepper to taste

Directions:

- Preheat grill to 400°F.

- Spot potatoes straightforwardly on stove rack in the focal point of the grill and prepare for 30 to 45 min.

- Evacuate and permit potatoes to cool for around 15 minutes.

- Cut every potato down the middle longwise and burrow every half out, scooping the potato substance into a blending bowl.

- Gather margarine and cream to the potato and pound into a single unit until smooth — season with salt and pepper and mix.

- Spread a portion of the potato blend into the base of each emptied potato skin and sprinkle with one tablespoon cheddar (you may make them remain pounded potato left to snack on).

- Add bacon to every half and top with a raw egg.

- Spot potatoes onto a heating sheet and come back to the appliance.

- Lower broiler temperature to 375°F and heat potatoes until egg whites simply set and yolks are as yet runny.

- Top every potato with a sprinkle of the rest of the cheddar, season with salt and pepper and finish with cut chives.

Nutrition:

- Calories: 647 kcal

- Protein: 30.46 g

- Fat: 55.79 g

- Carbohydrates: 7.45 g

4

Sirt Muesli

Preparation time: 30 minutes

Cooking time: 0 minutes

Servings: 2

Ingredients:

- 20g buckwheat drops

- 10g buckwheat puffs

- 15g coconut drops or dried up coconut

- 40g Medjool dates, hollowed and slashed

- 15g pecans, slashed

- 10g cocoa nibs

- 100g strawberries, hulled and slashed

- 100g plain Greek yoghurt (or vegetarian elective, for example, soya or coconut yoghurt)

Directions:

- Blend all the ingredients then put strawberries and yoghurt.

- Serve immediately.

Nutrition:

- Calories: 334 kcal

- Protein: 4.39 g

- Fat: 22.58 g

- Carbohydrates: 34.35 g

5

Spiced Scramble

Preparation time: 5 minutes

Cooking time: 5 minutes

Servings: 1

Ingredients:

- 25g (1oz) kale, finely chopped

- 2 eggs

- 1 spring onion (scallion) finely chopped

- 1 teaspoon turmeric

- 1 tablespoon olive oil

- Sea salt

- Freshly ground black pepper

Directions:

- Crack the eggs into a bowl. Add the turmeric and whisk them and season with salt and pepper.

- Heat the oil in a frying pan, add the kale and spring onions (scallions) and cook until it has wilted.

- Pour in the beaten eggs and stir until eggs have scrambled together with the kale.

Nutrition:

- Calories: 218

- Total Fat: 15.3 g

- Cholesterol: 386.9 mg

- Sodium: 656.2 mg

- Potassium: 243.0 mg

- Carbohydrates: 2.8 g

- Protein: 17.4 g

6

Cheesy Baked Eggs

Preparation time: 5 minutes

Cooking time: 15 minutes

Servings: 4

Ingredients:

- 4 large eggs

- 75g (3oz) cheese, grated

- 25g (1oz) fresh rocket (arugula) leaves, finely chopped

- 1 tablespoon parsley

- ½ teaspoon ground turmeric

- 1 tablespoon olive oil

Directions:

- Grease each ramekin dish with a little olive oil. Divide the rocket (arugula) between the ramekin dishes then break an egg into each one.

- Sprinkle a little parsley and turmeric on top then sprinkle on the cheese.

- Place the ramekins in a preheated oven at 220C/425F for 15 minutes, until the eggs are set and the cheese is bubbling.

Nutrition:

- Calories: 67

- Total Fat: 4 g

- Cholesterol: 12 mg

- Sodium: 265 mg

- Potassium: 84 mg

- Total Carbohydrates: 0.2 g

- Protein: 8 g

7

Chilled Strawberry and Walnut Porridge

Preparation time: 10 minutes

Cooking time: 12 hours

Servings: 1

Ingredients:

- 100g (3½ oz) strawberries

- 50g (2oz) rolled oats

- 4 walnut halves, chopped

- 1 teaspoon chia seeds

- 200mls (7fl oz) unsweetened soya milk

- 100ml (3½ oz) water

Directions:

- Place the strawberries, oats, soya milk and water into a blender and process until smooth.

- Stir in the chia seeds and mix well.

- Chill in the fridge overnight and serve in the morning with a sprinkling of chopped walnuts. It's simple and delicious.

Nutrition:

- Calories: 242

- Total Fat: 6 g

- Cholesterol: 1.3 mg

- Sodium: 37 mg

- Potassium: 207 mg

- Carbohydrates: 45 g

- Protein: 6 g

8

Strawberry & Nut Granola

Preparation time: 10 minutes

Cooking time: 50 minutes

Servings: 12

Ingredients:

- 200g (7oz) oats

- 250g (9oz) buckwheat flakes

- 100g (3½ oz) walnuts, chopped

- 100g (3½ oz) almonds, chopped

- 100g (3½ oz) dried strawberries

- 1½ teaspoons ground ginger

- 1½ teaspoons ground cinnamon

- 120mls (4fl oz) olive oil

- 2 tablespoon honey

Directions:

- Combine the oats, buckwheat flakes, nuts, ginger and cinnamon.

- In a saucepan, warm the oil and honey. Stir until the honey has melted.

- Pour the warm oil into the dry ingredients and mix well.

- Spread the mixture out on a large baking tray (or two) and bake in the oven at 150C (300F) for around 50 minutes until the granola is golden.

- Allow it to cool. Add in the dried berries.

Nutrition:

- Calories: 220

- Fat: 3 g

- Carbohydrates: 44 g

- Protein: 6 g

-

9

Strawberry Buckwheat Pancakes

Preparation time: 10 minutes

Cooking time: 20 minutes

Servings: 4

Ingredients:

- 100g (3½oz) strawberries, chopped

- 100g (3½ oz) buckwheat flour

- 1 egg

- 250mls (8fl oz) milk

- 1 teaspoon olive oil

- 1 teaspoon olive oil for frying

- Freshly squeezed juice of 1 orange

Directions:

- Pour the milk into a bowl and mix in the egg and a teaspoon of olive oil.

- Sift in the flour to the liquid mixture until smooth and creamy.

- Allow it to rest for 15 minutes. Heat a little oil in a pan and pour in a quarter of the mixture (or to the size you prefer.)

- Sprinkle in a quarter of the strawberries into the batter.

- Cook for around 2 minutes on each side.

- Serve hot with a drizzle of orange juice.

- You could try experimenting with other berries such as blueberries and blackberries.

Nutrition:

- Calories: 76

- Fat: 3 g

- Cholesterol: 26 mg

- Sodium: 184 mg

- Potassium: 17 mg

- Carbohydrates: 4 g

- Protein: 2 g

Poached Eggs & Rocket (Arugula)

Preparation time: 3 minutes

Cooking time: 5 minutes

Servings: 2

Ingredients:

- 2 eggs

- 25g (1oz) fresh rocket (arugula)

- 1 teaspoon olive oil

- Sea salt

- Freshly ground black pepper

Directions:

- Scatter the rocket (arugula) leaves onto a plate and drizzle the olive oil over them.

- Bring a shallow pan of water to the boil, add in the eggs and cook until the whites become firm.

- Serve the eggs on top of the rocket and season with salt and pepper.

Nutrition:

- Calories: 166

- Total Fat: 10 g

- Total Carbohydrates: 7 g

- Protein: 12 g

10

Chocolate Berry Blend

Preparation time: 5 minutes

Cooking time: 5 minutes

Servings: 1

Ingredients:

- 50g (2oz) blueberries

- 50g (2oz) strawberries

- 1 tablespoon 100% cocoa powder or cacao nibs

- 200mls (7fl oz) unsweetened soya milk

Directions:

- Place all of the ingredients into a blender with enough water to cover them and process until smooth.

Nutrition:

- Calories: 150

- Fat: 9 g

- Sodium: 30 mg

- Carbohydrates: 17 g

- Protein: 3 g

- Fiber: 2 g

- Sugar: 14 g

11

Mushroom & Red Onion Buckwheat Pancakes

Preparation time: 5 minutes

Cooking time: 10 minutes

Servings: 2

Ingredients:

For the pancakes:

- 125g (4oz) buckwheat flour

- 1 egg

- 150mls (5fl oz) semi-skimmed milk

- 150mls (5fl oz) water

- 1 teaspoon olive oil for frying

For the filling:

- 1 red onion, chopped

- 75g (3½ oz) mushrooms, sliced

- 50g (2oz) spinach leaves

- 1 tablespoon fresh parsley, chopped

- 1 teaspoon olive oil

- 50g (2oz) rocket (arugula) leaves

Directions:

- Sift the flour into a bowl and mix in an egg.

- Pour in the milk and water and mix to a smooth batter. Set aside.

- Heat a teaspoon of olive oil in a pan. Add the onion and mushrooms and cook for 5 minutes.

- Add the spinach and allow it to wilt. Set aside and keep it warm. Heat a teaspoon of oil in a frying pan and pour in half of the batter.

- Cook for 2 minutes on each side until golden.

- Spoon the spinach and mushroom mixture onto the pancake and add the parsley.

- Fold it over and serve onto a scattering of rocket (arugula) leaves. Repeat for the remaining mixture.

Nutrition:

- Calories: 109

- Fat: 5 g

- Sodium: 61 mg

- Potassium: 339 mg

- Carbohydrates: 34 g

- Protein: 6 g

12

Cream of Broccoli & Kale Soup

Preparation time: 10 minutes

Cooking time: 30 minutes

Servings: 4

Ingredients:

- 250g (9oz) broccoli

- 250g (9oz) kale

- 1 potato, peeled and chopped

- 1 red onion, chopped

- 600mls (1 pint) vegetable stock

- 300mls (½ pint) milk

- 1 tablespoon olive oil

- Sea salt

- Freshly ground black pepper

Directions:

- Heat the olive oil in a saucepan, add the onion and cook for 5 minutes.

- Add in the potato, kale and broccoli and cook for 5 minutes.

- Pour in the stock (broth) and milk and simmer for 20 minutes.

- Using a food processor or hand blender, process the soup until smooth and creamy.

- Season it with salt and pepper.

Nutrition:

- Calories: 123

- Total Fat: 7 g

- Cholesterol: 16 mg

- Sodium: 528 mg

- Potassium: 667 mg

- Total Carbohydrates: 13.4 g

- Protein: 5 g

French Onion Soup

Preparation time: 10 minutes

Cooking time: 55 minutes

Servings: 4

Ingredients:

- 750g (1¾ lbs) red onions, thinly sliced

- 50g (2oz) Cheddar cheese, grated (shredded)

- 12g (½ oz) butter

- 2 teaspoons flour

- 2 slices Wholemeal bread

- 900mls (1½ pints) beef stock (broth)

- 1 tablespoon olive oil

Directions:

- Heat the butter and oil in a large pan. Add the onions and gently cook on a low heat for 25 minutes, stirring occasionally.

- Add in the flour and stir well. Pour in the stock (broth) and keep stirring.

- Bring to the boil, reduce the heat and simmer for 30 minutes.

- Cut the slices of bread into triangles, sprinkle with cheese and place them under a hot grill (broiler) until the cheese has melted.

- Serve the soup into bowls and add 2 triangles of cheesy toast on top. Enjoy.

Nutrition:

- Calories: 290

- Total Fat: 9 g

- Total Carbohydrates: 33 g

- Protein: 17 g

Cheesy Buckwheat Cakes

Preparation time: 4 minutes

Cooking time: 4 minutes

Servings: 2

Ingredients:

- 100g (3½oz) buckwheat, cooked and cooled

- 1 large egg

- 25g (1oz) cheddar cheese, grated (shredded)

- 25g (1oz) Wholemeal breadcrumbs

- 2 shallots, chopped

- 2 tablespoons fresh parsley, chopped

- 1 tablespoon olive oil

Directions:

- Crack the egg into a bowl, whisk it then set aside. In a separate bowl combine all the buckwheat, cheese, shallots and parsley and mix well.

- Pour in the beaten egg to the buckwheat mixture and stir well.

- Shape the mixture into patties. Scatter the breadcrumbs on a plate and roll the patties in them. Heat the olive oil in a large frying pan and gently place the cakes in the oil.

- Cook for 3-4 minutes on either side until slightly golden.

Nutrition:

- Calories: 240

- Total Fat: 4 g

- Sodium: 380 mg

- Total Carbohydrates: 40 g

- Protein: 11 g

Lentil Soup

Preparation time: 5 minutes

Cooking time: 55 minutes

Servings: 4

Ingredients:

- 175g (6oz) red lentils

- 1 red onion, chopped

- 1 clove of garlic, chopped

- 2 sticks of celery, chopped

- 2 carrots, chopped

- ½ bird eye chili

- 1 teaspoon ground cumin

- 1 teaspoon ground turmeric

- 1 teaspoon ground coriander (cilantro)

- 1200mls (2 pints) vegetable stock (broth)

- 2 tablespoons olive oil

- Sea salt

- Freshly ground black pepper

Directions:

- Heat the oil in a saucepan and add the onion and cook for 5 minutes.

- Add in the carrots, lentils, celery, chili, coriander (cilantro), cumin, turmeric and garlic and cook for 5 minutes.

- Pour in the stock (broth), bring it to the boil, reduce the heat and simmer for 45 minutes.

- Using a hand blender or food processor, puree the soup until smooth.

- Season it with salt and pepper. Serve.

Nutrition:

- Calories: 194

- Total Fat: 1 g

- Sodium: 231 mg

- Total Carbohydrates: 34 g

- Protein: 13

- Fiber: 2 g

Apple Pancakes

Preparation time: 15 minutes

Cooking time: 24 minutes

Servings: 6

Ingredients:

- ½ cup buckwheat flour

- 2 tablespoons coconut sugar

- 1 teaspoon baking powder

- ½ teaspoon ground cinnamon

- 1/3 cup unsweetened almond milk

- 1 egg, beaten lightly

- 2 granny smith apples, peeled, cored, and grated

Directions:

- In a bowl, place the flour, coconut sugar, and cinnamon, and mix well.

- In another bowl, place the almond milk and egg and beat until well combined.

- Now, place the flour mixture and mix until well combined.

- Fold in the grated apples.

- Heat a lightly greased non-stick wok over medium-high heat.

- Add desired amount of mixture and with a spoon, spread into an even layer.

- Cook for 1–2 minutes on each side.

- Repeat with the remaining mixture.

- Serve warm with the drizzling of honey.

Nutrition:

- Calories 93

- Total Fat 2.1 g

- Saturated Fat 1 g

- Cholesterol 27 mg

- Sodium 23 mg

- Total Carbohydrates 22 g

- Fiber 3 g

- Sugar 12.1 g

- Protein 2.5 g

Matcha Pancakes

Preparation time: 15 minutes

Cooking time: 24 minutes

Servings: 6

Ingredients:

- 2 tablespoons flax meal

- 5 tablespoons warm water

- 1 cup spelt flour

- 1 cup buckwheat flour

- 1 tablespoon matcha powder

- 1 tablespoon baking powder

- Pinch of salt

- ¾ cup unsweetened almond milk

- 1 tablespoon olive oil

- 1 teaspoon vanilla extract

- 1/3 cup raw honey

Directions:

- In a bowl, add the flax meal and warm water and mix well. Set aside for about 5 minutes.

- In another bowl, place the flours, matcha powder, baking powder, and salt, and mix well.

- In the bowl of flax meal mixture, place the almond milk, oil, and vanilla extract, and beat until well combined.

- Now, place the flour mixture and mix until a smooth textured mixture is formed.

- Heat a lightly greased non-stick wok over medium-high heat.

- Add desired amount of mixture and with a spoon, spread into an even layer.

- Cook for about 2–3 minutes.

- Carefully, flip the side and cook for about 1 minute.

- Repeat with the remaining mixture.

- Serve warm with the drizzling of honey.

Nutrition:

- Calories 232

- Total Fat 4.6 g

- Saturated Fat 0.6 g

- Cholesterol 0 mg

- Sodium 56 mg

- Total Carbohydrates 46.3 g

- Fiber 5.3 g

- Sugar 16.2 g

- Protein 6 g

Chocolate Muffins

Preparation time: 15 minutes

Cooking time: 20 minutes

Servings: 6

Ingredients:

- ½ cup buckwheat flour

- ½ cup almond flour

- 4 tablespoons arrowroot powder

- 4 tablespoons cacao powder

- 1 teaspoon baking powder

- ½ teaspoon bicarbonate soda

- ½ cup boiled water

- 1/3 cup maple syrup

- 1/3 cup coconut oil, melted

- 1 tablespoon apple cider vinegar

- ½ cup unsweetened dark chocolate chips

Directions:

- Preheat your oven to 350°F. Line 6 cups of a muffin tin with paper liners.

- In a bowl, place the flours, arrowroot powder, baking powder, and bicarbonate of soda, and mix well.

- In a separate bowl, place the boiled water, maple syrup, and coconut oil, and beat until well combined.

- Now, place the flour mixture and mix until just combined.

- Gently, fold in the chocolate chips.

- Transfer the mixture into prepared muffin cups evenly.

- Bake for about 20 minutes, or until a toothpick inserted in the center comes out clean.

- Remove the muffin tin from oven and place onto a wire rack to cool for about 10 minutes.

- Carefully invert the muffins onto the wire rack to cool completely before serving.

Nutrition:

- Calories 410

- Total Fat 28.6 g

- Saturated Fat 17.8 g

- Sodium 25 mg

- Total Carbohydrates 32.5 g

- Fiber 5.8 g

- Protein 4.6 g

Kale & Mushroom Frittata

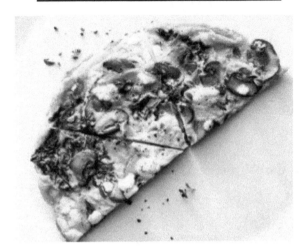

Preparation time: 15 minutes

Cooking time: 30 minutes

Servings: 5

Ingredients:

- 8 eggs

- ½ cup unsweetened almond milk

- Salt and ground black pepper, to taste

- 1 tablespoon olive oil

- 1 onion, chopped

- 1 garlic clove, minced

- 1 cup fresh mushrooms, chopped

- 1½ cups fresh kale, tough ribs removed and chopped

Directions:

- Preheat oven to 350°F.

- In a large bowl, place the eggs, coconut milk, salt, and black pepper, and beat well. Set aside.

- In a large ovenproof wok, heat the oil over medium heat and sauté the onion and garlic for about 3–4 minutes.

- Add the squash, kale, bell pepper, salt, and black pepper, and cook for about 8–10 minutes.

- Stir in the mushrooms and cook for about 3–4 minutes.

- Add the kale and cook for about 5 minutes.

- Place the egg mixture on top evenly and cook for about 4 minutes, without stirring.

- Transfer the wok in the oven and bake for about 12–15 minutes or until desired doneness.

- Remove from the oven and place the frittata side for about 3–5 minutes before serving.

- Cut into desired sized wedges and serve.

Nutrition:

- Calories 151

- Total Fat 10.2 g

- Saturated Fat 2.6 g

- Cholesterol 262 mg

- Sodium 158 mg

- Total Carbohydrates 5.6 g

- Fiber 1 g

- Sugar 1.7 g

- Protein 10.3 g

Kale, Apple, and Cranberry Salad

Preparation time: 10 minutes

Cooking time: 15 minutes

Servings: 4

Ingredients:

- 6 cups fresh baby kale

- 3 large apples, cored and sliced

- ¼ cup unsweetened dried cranberries

- ¼ cup almonds, sliced

108

- 2 tablespoons extra-virgin olive oil

- 1 tablespoon raw honey

- Salt and ground black pepper, to taste

Directions:

- In a salad bowl, place all the ingredients and toss to coat well.

- Serve immediately.

Nutrition:

- Calories 253

- Total Fat 10.3 g

- Saturated Fat 1.2 g

- Cholesterol 0 mg

- Sodium 84 mg

- Total Carbohydrates 40.7 g

- Fiber 6.6 g

- Sugar 22.7 g

Sirt Diet Recipes for Lunch

by

Lara Middleton

114

Table of Contents

Sticky Chicken Watermelon Noodle Salad

Preparation time: 15 minutes

Cooking time: 20 minutes

Servings: 1

Ingredients:

- 2 pieces of skinny rice noodles

- 1/2 tbsp. sesame oil

- 2 cups Water Melon

- Head of bib lettuce

- Half of a Lot of scallions

- Half of a Lot of fresh cilantro

- 2 skinless, boneless chicken breasts

- 1/2 tbsp. Chinese five-spice
- 1 tbsp. extra virgin olive oil
- 2 tbsp. sweet skillet
- 1 tbsp. sesame seeds
- A couple of cashews - smashed
- Dressing - could be made daily or 2 until
- 1 tbsp. low-salt soy sauce
- 1 teaspoon sesame oil
- 1 tbsp. peanut butter
- Half of a refreshing red chili
- Half of a couple of chives
- Half of a couple of cilantro
- Inch limes - juiced
- 1 small spoonful of garlic

Direction:

- In a bowl completely substitute the noodles in boiling drinking water. They are going to soon be carried out in 2 minutes.

- On a big sheet of parchment paper, then throw the chicken with pepper, salt, and also the five-spice.

- Twist over the newspaper, subsequently celebration and put the chicken using a rolling pin.

- Place into the large skillet with 1 tbsp. of olive oil, turning 3 or 4 minutes, until well charred and cooked through.

- Drain the noodles and toss with 1 tbsp. of sesame oil onto a sizable serving dish.

- Place 50% the noodles into the moderate skillet, stirring frequently until crispy and nice.

- Eliminate the Watermelon skin, then slice the flesh to inconsistent balls and then increase the platter.

- Reduce the lettuces and cut into small wedges and also half of a whole lot of leafy greens and scatter the dish.

- Place another 1 / 2 the cilantro pack, the soy sauce, coriander, chives, peanut butter, and a dab of water, 1 teaspoon of sesame oil, and the lime juice then mix till smooth.

- Set the chicken back to heat, garnish with the entire sweet skillet (or my walnut syrup mixture), and toss with the sesame seeds.

- Pour the dressing on the salad toss gently with fresh fingers until well coated, then add crispy noodles and then smashed cashews.

- Blend chicken pieces and add them to the salad.

Nutrition:

- Calories: 694
- Total Fat: 33 g
- Total Carbohydrates: 22 g
- Protein: 14 g

Lamb, Butternut Squash and Date Tagine

Preparation time: 5 minutes

Cooking time: 1 hour and 15 minutes

Servings: 4

Ingredients:

- 2 Tsps. coconut oil

- 1 Red onion, chopped

- 2cm ginger, grated

- 3 Garlic cloves, crushed or grated

- 1 teaspoon chili flakes (or to taste)

- 2 tsp. cumin seeds

- 2 teaspoons ground turmeric

- 1 cinnamon stick

- 800g lamb neck fillet, cut into 2cm chunks

- 1/2 tsp. salt

- 100g Medjool dates, pitted and sliced

- 400g Tin chopped berries, and half of a can of plain water

- 500g Butternut squash, chopped into 1cm cubes

- 400g Tin chickpeas, drained

- 2 tsp. fresh coriander (and extra for garnish)

- Buckwheat, Couscous, flatbread or rice to function

Directions:

- Pre heat the oven to 140C.

- Drizzle roughly 2 tbsps. coconut oil into a large ovenproof saucepan or cast-iron casserole dish.

- Add the chopped onion and cook on a gentle heat, with the lid for around five minutes, until the onions are softened but not too brown.

- Insert the grated ginger and garlic, chili, cumin, cinnamon, and garlic. Stir well and cook 1 minute with off the lid. Add a dash of water when it becomes too humid.

- Add from the lamb balls. Stir to coat the beef from the spices and onions, and then add the salt chopped meats and berries and roughly half of a can of plain water (100-200ml).

- Bring the tagine into the boil and put the lid and put on your skillet for about 1 hour and fifteen minutes.

- Add the chopped butternut squash and drained chickpeas. Stir everything together, place the lid back and go back to the oven to the last half an hour of cooking.

- When the tagine is able to remove from the oven and then stir fry throughout the chopped coriander.

Nutrition:

- Calories: 317
- Total Fat: 18 g
- Total Carbohydrates: 14 g
- Protein: 22 g

Turmeric Baked Salmon

Preparation time: 10 minutes

Cooking time: 10 minutes

Servings: 1

Ingredients:

- 125-150 g Skinned Salmon
- 1 tsp. extra virgin coconut oil
- 1 tsp. Ground turmeric
- 1/4 Juice of a lemon
- 1 tsp. extra virgin coconut oil
- 40 g Red onion, finely chopped
- 60 g Tinned green peas

- 1 Garlic clove, finely chopped
- 1 Cm fresh ginger, finely chopped
- 1 Bird's eye chili, finely chopped
- 150 g Celery cut into 2cm lengths
- 1 tsp. darkened curry powder
- 130 g Tomato, cut into 8 wedges
- 100 ml vegetable or pasta stock
- 1 tbsp. parsley, chopped

Directions:

- Heat the oven to 200C / gas mark 6.
- Start using the hot celery. Heat a skillet over a moderate --low heat, then add the olive oil then the garlic, onion, ginger, celery, and peppermint.
- Fry lightly for 2-3 minutes until softened but not colored, you can add the curry powder and cook for a further minute.
- Insert the berries afterward, your lentils and stock, and simmer for 10 seconds. You might choose to increase or reduce the cooking time according to how crunchy you'd like your own sausage.
- Meanwhile, mix the garlic olive oil and lemon juice and then rub the salmon.

- Set on the baking dish and cook 8 – 10 seconds.
- In order to complete, stir the skillet throughout the celery and function with the salmon.

Nutrition:

- Calories: 205
- Total Fat: 14 g
- Cholesterol: 47 mg
- Sodium: 622.0 mg
- Potassium: 487 mg
- Total Carbohydrates: 2 g
- Protein: 18 g

-

Prawn Arrabiata

Preparation time: 15 minutes

Cooking time: 35 minutes

Servings:

Ingredients:

- 125-150 g Beef or cooked prawns (Ideally king prawns)
- 65 g Buckwheat pasta
- 1 tablespoon extra-virgin coconut oil

Arrabiata sauce

- 40 g Red onion, finely chopped
- 1 Garlic clove, finely chopped
- 30 g celery, thinly sliced

- 1 Bird's eye chili, finely chopped

- 1 tsp. Dried mixed veggies

- 1 tsp. extra virgin coconut oil

- 2 Tablespoon White wine (optional)

- 400 Gram tinned chopped berries

- 1 tbsp. Chopped parsley

Directions:

- Fry the garlic, onion, celery, and peppermint and peppermint blossoms at the oil over moderate-low heat for 1- 2 weeks.

- Turn up the heat to medium, bring the wine and cook 1 second.

- Add the berries and leave the sauce simmer over moderate-low heat for 20 to half an hour, until it's a great rich texture. In the event you're feeling that the sauce is becoming too thick, simply put in just a very little water.

- As the sauce is cooking, attract a bowl of water to the boil and then cook the pasta as per the package directions. Once cooked to your dish, drain, then toss with the olive oil and also maintain at the pan before needed.

- If you're utilizing raw prawns, put them into your sauce and cook for a further 3 - 4 minutes, till they've turned opaque and pink, and then add the parsley and function. If you're using cooked prawns, insert them using the skillet, and then bring the sauce to the boil and then function.

- Add the cooked pasta into the sauce, then mix thoroughly but lightly and function.

Nutrition:

- Calories: 415
- Total Fat: 10 g
- Total Carbohydrates: 57 g
- Protein: 23 g

Baked Potatoes with Spicy Chickpea Stew

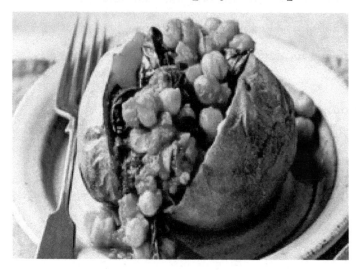

Preparation time: 10 minutes

Cooking time: 1 hour

Servings: 4 - 6

Ingredients:

- 4 - 6 Celery, pricked all over

- 2 tsp. coconut oil

- 2 Red onions, finely chopped

- 4 Cloves garlic, crushed or grated

- 2cm ginger, grated

- 1/2 -2 teaspoons chili flakes (depending on how hot you enjoy stuff)

- 2 tablespoons cumin seeds

- 2 tsp. turmeric

- Splash Of water

- 2 x 400g tins chopped tomatoes

- 2 tablespoons unsweetened cocoa powder (or even cacao)

- 2 X 400g tins chickpeas including the chick-pea water, do not drain

- 2 Yellow peppers (or any color you would like), chopped into bite size pieces

- 2 tablespoons parsley and extra for garnish

- Salt And pepper to taste (optional)

- Negative Salad (discretionary)

Directions:

- Pre heat the oven to 200C, however, you are able to prepare all of your own ingredients.

- When the oven is still hot enough to set your lemon potatoes from the oven and cook for 1 hour or so until they do the way you prefer them.

- Once the potatoes come from the oven, then place the coconut oil and sliced red onion into a large wide saucepan and cook lightly, with the lid for five minutes until the onions are tender but not brown.

- Remove the lid and then add the ginger, garlic, cumin, and simmer. Cook for a further minute on very low heat, then add the garlic and a tiny dab of water and then cook for another moment; just take care never to allow the pan to get too tender.

- Add from the berries, cocoa powder (or even cacao), chickpeas (including the chickpea water) and salt.

- Allow to the boil, and then simmer on a very low heat for 4-5 seconds before the sauce is thick and unctuous (but do not allow it to burn up). The stew ought to be performed at exactly the exact same period as the legumes.

- Finally, Stir at the two tbsp. of parsley, plus a few pepper and salt if you desire, and also serve the stew in addition to the chopped sausage, possibly with a very simple salad.

Nutrition:
- Calories: 348
- Total Fat: 17 g
- Sodium: 148 mg
- Potassium: 312 mg
- Total Carbohydrates: 41 g
- Protein: 7 g

•

135

Char-grilled Steak

Preparation time:

Cooking time:

Servings:

Ingredients:

- 5g parsley, finely chopped
- 100g potatoes, peeled and cut into 2cm dice
- 50g Lettuce, chopped
- 1 tbsp. extra virgin coconut oil
- 50g Red onion, chopped into circles
- 1 garlic clove, finely chopped

- 120 - 150g 3.5cm thick beef noodle beef or 2cm-thick sirloin beef
- 40ml Red wine
- 150ml Beef inventory
- 1 tsp. tomato purée
- 1 tsp. corn flour, dissolved in 1 tablespoon water

Direction:

- Heating the oven to 220°C
- Put the sausage in a saucepan of boiling water, then return to the boil and then cook 4 minutes, then empty.
- Put in a skillet with 1 tbsp. of the oil and then roast in the oven for 4 – 5 minutes. Twist the berries every 10 minutes to ensure even cooking. After cooking, remove from the oven, sprinkle with the chopped parsley, and mix well.
- Fry the onion 1 tsp. of the oil over a moderate heat for 5 minutes until tender and well caramelized.
- Maintain heat. Steam the kale for 2 - 3 minutes. Stir the garlic lightly in 1/2 tsp. of oil for 1 minute until tender but not colored. Insert the spinach and simmer for a further 1--two minutes, until tender. Maintain heat.
- Heat ovenproof skillet until smoking then laid the beef from 1/2 a tsp. of the oil. Then fry from the skillet over a

137

moderate-high temperature in accordance with just how you would like your beef done. If you prefer your beef moderate, it'd be wise to sear the beef and also transfer the pan into a toaster place in 220°C/petrol 7 and then finish the cooking which manner to your prescribed occasions.

- Remove the meat from the pan and put aside to break. Add your wine into the skillet to bring any meat up residue. Bubble to decrease the wine by half an hour until syrupy, along with a flavor that is concentrated.

- Insert the inventory and tomato purée into the beef pan and bring to the boil, add the corn flour paste to thicken your sauce, then adding it only a little at a time till you've got your preferred consistency.

- Stir in just about anyone of those juices out of the dinner that is rested and serve with the roasted lettuce, celery, onion rings, and red berry sauce.

Nutrition:

- Calories: 416
- Total Fat: 13 g
- Total Carbohydrates: 39 g
- Protein: 35 g

Fruity Curry Chicken Salad

Preparation time: 10 minutes

Cooking time: 10 minutes

Servings: 8

Ingredients

- 4 skinless, boneless chicken pliers - cooked and diced
- 1 tsp. celery, diced
- 4 green onions, sliced
- 1 golden delicious apple peeled, cored and diced
- 1/3 cup golden raisins
- 1/3 cup seedless green grapes, halved

- 1/2 cup sliced toasted pecans
- 1/8 tsp. Ground black pepper
- 1/2 tsp. curry powder
- 3/4 cup light mayonnaise

Directions:

- In a big bowl combine the chicken, onion, celery, apple, celery, celery, pecans, pepper, curry powder, and carrot. Mix altogether.

Nutrition:

- Calories: 156
- Total Fat: 6 g
- Total Carbohydrates: 10 g
- Protein: 14 g

Zuppa Toscana

Preparation time: 20 minutes

Cooking time: 1 hour

Servings: 2

Ingredients:

- 1 lb ground Italian sausage

- 1 1/4 tsp. crushed red pepper flakes

- 4 pieces bacon, cut into ½ inch bits

- 1 big onion, diced

- 1 tbsp. minced garlic

- 5 (13.75 oz) can chicken broth

- 6 celery, thinly chopped
- 1 cup thick cream
- 1/4 bunch fresh spinach, tough stems removed

Directions:

- Cook that the Italian sausage and red pepper flakes in a pot on medium-high heat until crumbly, browned, with no longer pink, 10 to 15minutes. Drain and put aside.
- Cook the bacon at the exact Dutch oven over moderate heat until crispy, about 10 minutes.
- Drain leaving a couple of tablespoons of drippings together with all the bacon at the bottom of the toaster. Stir in the garlic and onions cook until onions are tender and translucent, about 5 minutes.
- Pour the chicken broth to the pot with the onion and bacon mix; contribute to a boil on high temperature.
- Add the berries, and boil until fork-tender, about 20 minutes. Reduce heat to moderate and stir in the cream and also the cooked sausage – heat throughout. Mix the lettuce to the soup before serving.

Nutrition:

- Calories: 403

- Total Fat: 24 g

- Cholesterol: 66 mg

- Total Carbohydrates: 32 g

- Protein: 15 g

Turmeric Chicken & Kale Salad with Honey-Lime Dressing

Preparation time: 20 minutes

Cooking time: 10 minutes

Serves: 2

Ingredients:

For the chicken

- 1 tsp. ghee or 1 tablespoon coconut oil

- 1/2 moderate brown onion, diced

- 250 300 grams / 9 oz. Chicken mince or pops upward chicken thighs

- 1 large garlic clove, finely-chopped

- 1 tsp. turmeric powder

- Optional 1 teaspoon lime zest

- Juice of 1/2 lime

- 1/2 tsp. salt

For your salad:

- 6 broccoli 2 or two cups of broccoli florets

- 2 tbsp. pumpkin seeds (pepitas)

- 3 big kale leaves, stalks removed and sliced

- Optional 1/2 avocado, chopped

- Bunch of coriander leaves, chopped

- Couple of fresh parsley leaves, chopped

For your dressing:

- 3 tbsp. lime juice

- 1 small garlic clove, finely diced or grated

- 3 tbsp. extra virgin coconut oil

- 1 tsp. raw honey

- 1/2 tsp. whole grain or Dijon mustard

- 1/2 tsp. sea salt

Directions:

- Heat the ghee or coconut oil at a tiny skillet pan above medium-high heat. Bring the onion and then sauté on moderate heat for 45 minutes, until golden.

- Insert the chicken blossom and garlic and simmer for 2-3 minutes on medium-high heat, breaking it all out.

- Add the garlic, lime zest, lime juice, and salt and soda and cook stirring often, to get a further 3-4 minutes. Place the cooked mince aside.

- As the chicken is cooking, add a little spoonful of water. Insert the broccoli and cook 2 minutes. Rinse under warm water and then cut into 3-4 pieces each.

- Insert the pumpkin seeds into the skillet out of the toast and chicken over moderate heat for two minutes, stirring often to avoid burning and season with a little salt. Set aside. Raw pumpkin seeds will also be nice to utilize.

- Put chopped spinach at a salad bowl and then pour over the dressing table. With the hands, massage and toss the carrot with the dressing table. This will dampen the lettuce, a lot similar to what citrus juice will not steak or fish Carpaccio– it "hamburgers" it marginally.

- Finally, toss throughout the cooked chicken, broccoli, fresh herbs, pumpkin seeds, and avocado pieces.

Nutrition:

- Calories: 418
- Total Fat: 21 g
- Total Carbohydrates: 10 g
- Protein: 46 g

Buckwheat Noodles with Chicken Kale & Miso Dressing

Preparation time: 15 minutes

Cooking time: 15 minutes

Serves: 2

Ingredients:

For the noodles:

- 2/3 handfuls of kale leaves (removed from the stem and fully trimmed)
- 150 g / 5 oz buckwheat noodles (100 percent buckwheat, no wheat)

- 34 shiitake mushrooms, chopped

- 1 tsp. coconut oil or ghee

- 1 brown onion, finely diced

- 1 moderate free-range chicken, chopped or diced

- 1 red chili, thinly chopped (seeds out based on how hot you want it)

- 2 large garlic cloves, finely-chopped

- 23 tbsp. tamari sauce (fermented soy sauce)

For your miso dressing:

- 1 ½ tbsp. fresh organic miso

- 1 tbsp. tamari sauce

- 1 tbsp. peppermint oil

- 1 tbsp. lime or lemon juice

- 1 tsp. sesame oil (optional)

Directions:

- Bring a medium saucepan of water. Insert the kale and cook 1 minute, until slightly wilted.

- Remove and put aside but keep the water and put it back to boil. Insert the soba noodles and cook according to the package directions (usually about five minutes).

- Rinse under warm water and place aside. Pan press the shiitake mushrooms at just a very little ghee or coconut oil (about a tsp.) for 23 minutes, until lightly browned on each side. Sprinkle with sea salt and then place aside.

- In the exact skillet, warm olive oil ghee over medium-high heating system. Sauté onion and simmer for 2 3 minutes and add the chicken bits.

- Cook five minutes over medium heat; stirring a few days, you can put in the garlic, tamari sauce and just a tiny dab of water. Cook for a further 2-3 minutes, stirring often until chicken is cooked through.

- Add the carrot and soba noodles and chuck throughout the chicken to heat up.

- Mix the miso dressing and scatter on the noodles before eating; in this manner, you can retain dozens of enzymes that are beneficial at the miso.

Nutrition:
- Calories: 190
- Total Fat: 0.5 g
- Sodium: 420 mg

- Total Carbohydrates: 38 mg

- Protein: 8 g

Kale and Red Onion Dhal with Buckwheat

Preparation time: 5 minutes

Cooking time: 25 minutes

Servings: 4

Ingredients:

- 1 tbsp. coconut oil
- 1 small red onion, chopped
- 3 garlic cloves, crushed or grated
- 2 cm lemon, grated
- 1birds eye chili deseeded and finely chopped
- 2 tsp. turmeric
- 2 teaspoons garam masala

- 160g red lentils

- 400ml coconut milk

- 200ml water

- 100g kale (or lettuce is a terrific alternative)

- 160g buckwheat (or brown rice)

Directions:

- Put the coconut oil in a large, deep saucepan and then add the chopped onion. Cook on very low heat, with the lid for five minutes until softened.

- Insert the ginger, garlic, and chili and cook 1 minute.

- Insert the garlic, garam masala and a dash of water and then cook for 1 minute.

- Insert the reddish peas, coconut milk, and also 200ml water (try so only by half filling the coconut milk could with water and stirring it in the saucepan).

- Mix everything together thoroughly and then cook for 20 minutes over a lightly heat with the lid. Stir occasionally and add just a little bit more water in case the dhal starts to stick.

- After 20 seconds, add the carrot, stir thoroughly and then replace the lid, then cook for a further five minutes (1-2 minutes if you are using spinach)

- Around 1-5 minutes ahead of the curry is ready, set the buckwheat at a medium saucepan and then put in lots of warm water. Bring back the water to the boil and then cook for 10 minutes (or only a little longer in case you would rather your buckwheat softer. Drain the buckwheat using a sieve and serve with the dhal.

- **Nutrition:**
- Calories: 151
- Total Fat: 3 g
- Sodium: 51.7 mg
- Potassium: 531 mg
- Total Carbohydrates: 23 g
- Protein: 10 g

Farinata with Zucchini and Shallot

Preparation time: 15 minutes

Cooking time: 40 minutes

Servings: 4

Ingredients:

- 400 ml of water
- 125 g of chickpea flour
- 60 g of Evo oil
- 8 g of salt
- 1 zucchini
- 1 shallot

Directions:

- Put the water in a container; gradually add the flour mixing with the whisk to avoid creating lumps.

- Add the oil, salt, chopped shallot, zucchini cut into rounds and keep stirring until the mixture is well blended.

- Pour it all into a round baking tray greased with a drizzle of oil. Cook at 250° for 30-40 minutes.

- Once it's out of the oven, let it cool before you serve it.

Nutrition:

- Calories: 129

- Total Fat: 6 g

- Sodium: 250 mg

- Potassium: 195 mg

- Total Carbohydrates: 13 g

- Protein: 5 g

Stuffed with Vegetables

Preparation time: 5 minutes

Cooking time: 15 minutes

Servings: 2

Ingredients:

- 4 large spoons of chickpea flour

- 2 level teaspoons of powdered vegetable broth preparation

- Sunflower seed oil

- 300 g mixed vegetables already cooked (e.g. a ratatouille or any other vegetable mix)

Directions:

- Mix with a whisk the chickpea flour and the powdered cube, adding water to obtain a rather liquid but still creamy consistency.

- Swirl the vegetables with a little sunflower oil and, once heated, pour the batter. For a crispier omelet, the batter layer must be only a few mm thick (maximum one cm, when the filling is abundant).

- Cook over low heat on one side until the top has thickened as well. At this point turn with the method you prefer and complete the cooking on the other side.

Nutrition:

- Calories: 171
- Total Fat: 5 g
- Sodium: 225 mg
- Potassium: 390 mg
- Total Carbohydrates: 25 g
- Protein: 5 g

-

Zucchini Dumplings

Preparation time: 15 minutes

Cooking time: 1 hour

Servings: 4

Ingredients:

- 2 zucchini

- 1 vegan puff pastry for savory pies

- 8 pitted green olives

- Sunflower seeds

- 1 onion

- Pepper

- Oil

Directions:

- Cut the zucchini into thin slices, put them in the non-stick pan with a drizzle of oil (very little) and simmer them with the lid for about 30 minutes, until well cooked.
- Roll out the puff pastry and divide it into 4 parts. Chop the olives; add the chopped onion and some sunflower seeds.
- In a small cup place some zucchini (just enough for a dumpling) and add a quarter of the chopped olives, mix and place on the puff pastry.
- Add pepper and a drizzle of oil. Repeat the operation for the 4 dumplings, then close them by joining the corners and bake for 30 minutes.
- You can also use other vegetables instead of zucchini.

Nutrition:

- Calories: 240
- Total Fat: 8 g
- Total Carbohydrates: 26 g
- Protein: 10 g

Sponge Beans with Onion

Preparation time: 5 minutes

Cooking time: 1 hour and 30 minutes

Servings: 2

Ingredients:

- 250 g boiled Spanish beans
- 1 red onion
- 1 tablespoon parsley
- Salt
- 2 tablespoons of oil
- 1 teaspoon of apple vinegar
- 1 teaspoon of dried oregano or 5 fresh oregano leaves

Directions:

- Cut the onion into thin slices and cook it for a minute with a tablespoon of water in the microwave at full power.

- Combine all the ingredients in a bowl and leave to rest a couple of hours before serving, stirring a couple of times so that the beans take on the flavour of the seasoning.

Nutrition:

- Calories: 250
- Total Fat: 7 g
- Total Carbohydrates: 36 g
- Protein: 5 g

Cannellini Beans

Preparation time: 5 minutes

Cooking time: 25 minutes

Servings: 1

Ingredients:

- 2 cloves of garlic, minced
- 2 sage leaves
- 2 tablespoons of extra virgin olive oil
- Boiled cannellini beans
- Fresh well ripe tomatoes
- Salt and pepper

Directions:

- Cook for 2-3 minutes in a pan with oil, garlic and sage.

- Then add the tomatoes, cut into segments, and let them brown for a couple of minutes.

- Add the beans, salt and pepper to taste, stir.

- Cook in a covered pot for 20 minutes, checking and turning occasionally. Serve hot.

Nutrition:

- Calories: 320

- Total Fat: 7 g

- Total Carbohydrates: 54 g

- Protein: 18 g

Diced Tofu and Lentils

Preparation time: 5 minutes

Cooking time: 30 minutes

Servings: 2

Ingredients:

- 200 g of tofu cake
- Soy sauce (shoyu)
- Extra virgin olive oil
- Onion
- Sprig of rosemary
- 2 tablespoons of chopped chili pepper

- 50 g of red lentils
- Vegetable stock
- Breadcrumbs

Directions:

- Marinate the diced tofu for half an hour in the soy sauce, adding a little water to cover it.
- In the meantime, boil the red lentils, washed in the vegetable stock for about 20 minutes, until they are soft enough and the stock has dried a bit.
- Sauté 2 tablespoons of chili pepper then diced onion and rosemary in olive oil until the onion is golden brown.
- Add the tofu with some of the marinating shoyu and after a few minutes also the lentils with very little broth.
- Let everything shrink with the lid and over low heat and to thicken add 2 tablespoons of breadcrumbs.

Nutrition:

- Calories: 63

- Total Fat: 3 g

- Total Carbohydrates: 2 g

- Fiber: 1 g

- Protein: 8 g

Seitan and Lentils

Preparation time: 5 minutes

Cooking time: 10 minutes

Servings: 2

Ingredients:

- 4 slices of seitan
- 1 box of lentils
- Half onion
- 1 tablespoon of soy cream
- Salt and pepper
- 1 tablespoon of extra virgin olive oil
- Handful of fresh parsley

- Turmeric (optional)

Directions:

- Chop the onion and cook it in oil. Cut the seitan into cubes.
- When it is well coloured - but not burnt - add the seitan cubes and, after a few minutes, add the lentils drained and well washed.
- Add salt and pepper and sauté with a little hot water.
- Finish with the cream, turmeric and chopped parsley, cook for a few more minutes and then serve with a nice fresh salad and toasted whole meal bread.

Nutrition:

- Calories: 120
- Total Fat: 6 g
- Total Carbohydrates: 15 g
- Protein: 60 g

Zucchini Croquettes

Preparation time: 5 minutes

Cooking time: 20 minutes

Servings: 3

Ingredients:

- 500 g zucchini
- 2 slices of bread box
- 2 tablespoons of yeast
- 2 tablespoons of breadcrumbs
- 4 tablespoons of oat flakes
- 1/2 glass of soya milk
- Nutmeg

Directions:

- Wash the zucchini, trim them and scratch them with the vegetable grater; dip the slices of bread in soy milk, heat over very low heat, squeeze them and add them to the zucchini.

- Add the baking powder, breadcrumbs, oatmeal flakes, nutmeg and salt.

- Mix well, form croquettes with wet hands, compact them well and fry in hot oil.

- Drain and serve hot. Raw zucchini tend to purge water, so if the mixture is too moist increase the quantity of oat flakes, otherwise these very delicate croquettes could flake during cooking.

Nutrition:

- Calories: 228
- Total Fat: 20 g
- Total Carbohydrates: 11 g
- Protein: 16 g

Leeks and Mushrooms Crepes

Preparation time: 5 minutes

Cooking time: 25 minutes

Servings: 2

Ingredients:

- 80 g white flour
- 20 g of chickpea flour
- 200 ml of soy milk
- 100 g of sliced and cooked champignons mushrooms
- 2 leeks (including the pale green part)
- Soya cream
- Chives

172

- Garlic powder

Directions:

- Mix the two flours in a bowl, and then add the milk a little at a time, stirring with a whisk to avoid the formation of lumps. At pleasure, salt the dough.
- Fry the thinly sliced leeks in a frying pan. When they are tender, add the mushrooms and stir for a few minutes.
- Add a little soy cream, let it set aside. In the meantime, prepare the crepes: oil a non-stick pan for crepes with the special brush and pour half the mixture, taking care to cover the entire surface of the pan in a thin layer.
- Let the other side cozy up, turn and cook too. Stuff it with half the stuffing and roll it up.
- Repeat the operation for the second crêpe. In a small bowl, mix soy cream with salt, pepper, chives and garlic powder.
- Pour the sauce over the pancakes when serving.

Nutrition:

- Calories: 160

- Total Fat: 4 g
- Sugar: 3 g
- Total Carbohydrates: 27 g
- Protein: 4 g

Herb Crepes

Preparation time: 5 minutes

Cooking time: 25 minutes

Servings: 2

Ingredients:

- 1/2 cup of flour
- 1/2 a cup of whole meal flour
- 3/4 glass of rice milk
- Spices to taste
- Bunch of chives
- Pinch of salt
- Pinch of pepper

- 1 tablespoon of oil

Directions:

- Mix all the ingredients in a bowl, starting with the solid ones, including chopped chives.
- Gradually add the rice milk until it reaches the right consistency (not too liquid or too thick; if necessary, stretch with a little water).
- Grease the pan with the oil you prefer or with a diced vegetable butter, pour one ladle of dough at a time, which will be cooked on both sides until it is golden brown.
- You can add a filling as you like or enjoy them naturally.

Nutrition:

- Calories: 150
- Total Fat: 5 g
- Total Carbohydrates: 25 g
- Protein: 5 g

Baked Cauliflower

Preparation time: 5 minutes

Cooking time: 20 minutes

Servings: 4

Ingredients:

- Cauliflower
- Red pepper
- Vegan béchamel or soy cream
- Handful of breadcrumbs
- Fresh chopped parsley
- Halls
- Herbs (optional)

Directions:

- Clean, wash and boil a cauliflower in salted water (a handful of salt). In the meantime, wash and roast a red pepper and, once ready and cooled, remove the skin, open it, clean it from the seeds, reduce it to rags and salt it.

- Proceed with the preparation of the vegan béchamel or, alternatively, use soya cream.

- Mix the cream and peppers and heat over low heat for 2 minutes, until the mixture is mixed. At discretion, combine herbs.

- Place the cauliflower in an earthenware bowl, pour over the cream with the peppers and proceed with a sprinkling of breadcrumbs and chopped fresh parsley. Put in the oven until golden brown.

Nutrition:

- Calories: 107

- Total Fat: 9 g
- Sodium: 740 mg
- Potassium: 180 mg
- Total Carbohydrates: 6 g
- Protein: 3 g

Tofu Sticks

Preparation time: 5 minutes

Cooking time: 15 minutes

Servings: 2

Ingredients:

- A brick of tofu
- 2 tablespoons of chickpea flour
- 2 tablespoons of corn flour
- 1 tablespoon of baking powder in flakes
- Salt, oregano, paprika oil to fry
- 1/2 lemon

Directions:

- Cut the tofu cake in order to obtain the 'sticks', that is slices 5cm long and about 1 cm thick.

- Prepare in a bowl a batter of water and chickpea flour thick enough.

- In another bowl mix corn flour and yeast flakes, adding a little salt, oregano, paprika (or other spices to taste).

- Pass the slices of tofu one by one in the chickpea batter and then in the corn flour with yeast flakes pressing well with your fingers to cover well.

- Heat the oil in a pan and brown them on both sides. After placing them on absorbent paper, spray with drops of lemon juice.

Nutrition:

- Calories: 84
- Total Fat: 4 g
- Sodium: 25 mg
- Potassium: 79 mg
- Total Carbohydrates: 5 g
- Protein: 7 g

Pizzaiola Steak

Preparation time: 10 minutes

Cooking time: 50 minutes

Servings: 2

Ingredients:

- 10 dehydrated soya steaks
- 1 onion
- 400 ml of tomato puree
- Evo oil
- Halls
- 1 pinch of whole cane sugar
- Oregano

Directions:

- Soak the soya steaks for 20-30 minutes (as they will float, after 10-15 minutes, turn them on the other side).

- Drain them well, pour them in a non-stick pan with some evo oil and chopped onion; brown them for a few minutes.

- Pour in the tomato puree, salt, sugar, a drop of water and cook it all covered for 15-20 minutes, stirring occasionally. If the tomato becomes too dry during cooking, add more water. When cooked, add some oregano.

Nutrition:

- Calories: 318
- Total Fat: 13 g
- Cholesterol: 50 mg
- Sodium: 600 mg
- Total Carbohydrates: 15 g
- Protein: 30 g

Chicken and Kale with Spicy Salsa

Preparation time: 10 minutes

Cooking time: 50 minutes

Servings: 1

Ingredients:

- 1 skinless, boneless chicken filet/breast
- ¼ cup buckwheat
- 1/4 lemon, juiced
- 1 tbsp. extra virgin olive oil
- 1 cup kale, chopped
- 1/2 red onion, sliced
- 1 tsp. fresh ginger, chopped

184

- 2 tsp. ground turmeric

Salsa:

- 1 tomato
- 3 sprigs of parsley, chopped
- 1 tbsp. chopped capers
- 1 chili, deseeded and minced use less if desired
- Juice of 1/4 lemon

Directions:

- Chop all ingredients above, just for the salsa, and set aside in a bowl.
- Pre-eat the oven to 425 F.
- Add a teaspoon of the turmeric, the lemon juice and a little oil to the chicken, cover and set aside for 10 minutes.
- In a hot pan, slide the chicken and marinade. Cook for 2-3 minutes each side, on high to sear it.
- Slide it all onto a baking-safe dish and for cook for about 20 minutes or until cooked.
- Lightly steam the kale in a steamer, or on the stovetop with a lid and some water, for about 5 minutes. You want to wilt the kale, not boil or burn it.

- Sautee the red onions and ginger, and after 4-5 minutes, add the cooked kale and stir for 1 minute.
- Cook the buckwheat, adding in the turmeric. Serve the chicken along with the buckwheat, kale, and spicy salsa.

Nutrition:

- Calories: 300
- Total Fat: 11 g
- Total Carbohydrates: 10 g
- Protein: 35 g

Shiitake Stew

Preparation time: 10 minutes

Cooking time: 3 – 4 hours

Servings: 8

Ingredients:

- 3 garlic cloves, minced
- 2 cups chopped onions
- 1/2 cup olive oil
- Salt & 1 tsp. ground pepper to taste
- 4 cups vegetable broth
- 2 pounds dry shiitake mushrooms

Directions:

- Put ingredients in the slow cooker. Cover and cook on low for 3 to 4 hours.

Nutrition:

- Calories: 140
- Total Fat: 3 g
- Total Carbohydrates: 30 g
- Protein: 5 g

Chili Con Carne

Preparation time: 5 minutes

Cooking Time: 45 minutes

Servings: 4

Ingredients:

- 1 red onion, chopped
- 3 cloves of garlic, finely chopped
- 2 Tai chilies, finely chopped
- 1 tablespoon of olive oil
- 1 tablespoon turmeric
- 1 tablespoon cumin
- 400g minced beef

- 150ml red wine

- 1 red pepper, seeded and diced

- 2 cans of small tomatoes (400ml each)

- 1 tablespoon of tomato paste

- 1 tablespoon cocoa powder without sugar

- 150g canned kidney beans, drained

- 300ml beef broth

- 5g coriander green, chopped

- 5g parsley, chopped

- 160g buckwheat

Directions:

- Sauté the onions, garlic and chilies in olive oil in a high frying pan or in a frying pan at medium heat. After three minutes add cumin and turmeric and stir.

- Then add the minced meat and fry until everything is brown. Add the red wine, bring to the boil and reduce by half.

- Add the peppers, tomatoes, tomato paste, cocoa, kidney beans and stock, stir and cook for an hour. Add a little water or broth if the chili is too dry.

- Cook buckwheat according to the Directions on the packet and serve sprinkled with the chilies and fresh herbs.

Nutrition:

- Calories: 101
- Total Fat: 3 g
- Cholesterol: 50 mg
- Total Carbohydrates: 10 g
- Protein: 11 g

Mussels in Red Wine Sauce

Preparation time: 5 minutes

Cooking Time: 50 minutes

Servings: 2

Ingredients:

- 800g 2lb mussels
- 2 x 400g 14 oz tins of chopped tomatoes
- 25g 1oz butter
- 1 tablespoon fresh chives, chopped
- 1 tablespoon fresh parsley, chopped
- 1 bird's-eye chili, finely chopped
- 4 cloves of garlic, crushed

- 400 ml 14fl. oz red wine

- Juice of 1 lemon

- 364 calories per serving

Directions:

- Wash the mussels, remove their beards and set them aside. Heat the butter in a large saucepan and add in the red wine.

- Reduce the heat and add the parsley, chives, chili and garlic whilst stirring. Add in the tomatoes, lemon juice and mussels.

- Cover the saucepan and cook for 2-3 minutes. Remove the saucepan from the heat and take out any mussels which haven't opened and discard them. Serve and eat immediately.

Nutrition:

- Calories: 380

- Total Fat: 15 g

- Cholesterol: 95 mg

- Total Carbohydrates: 17 g

- Protein: 35 g

Roast Balsamic Vegetables

Preparation time: 5 minutes

Cooking time: 45 minutes

Servings: 2

Ingredients:

- 4 tomatoes, chopped
- 2 red onions, chopped
- 3 sweet potatoes, peeled and chopped
- 100g 3½ oz red chicory or if unavailable, use yellow
- 100g 3½ oz kale, finely chopped
- 300g 11oz potatoes, peeled and chopped
- 5 stalks of celery, chopped
- 1 bird's-eye chili, de-seeded and finely chopped

- 2 tablespoons fresh parsley, chopped
- 2 tablespoons fresh coriander cilantro chopped
- 3 tablespoons olive oil
- 2 tablespoons balsamic vinegar 1 teaspoon mustard
- Sea salt
- Freshly ground black pepper
- 310 calories per serving

Directions:

- Place the olive oil, balsamic, mustard, parsley and coriander cilantro into a bowl and mix well.
- Toss all the remaining ingredients into the dressing and season with salt and pepper.
- Transfer the vegetables to an ovenproof dish and cook in the oven at 200C/400F for 45 minutes.

Nutrition:

- Calories: 123
- Total Fat: 3 g
- Sodium: 45 mg
- Total Carbohydrates: 24 g
- Protein: 5 g

Honey Chili Squash

Preparation time: 5 minutes

Cooking time: 20 minutes

Servings: 2

Ingredients:

- 2 red onions, roughly chopped 2.5cm
- 1 inch chunk of ginger root, finely chopped
- 2 cloves of garlic
- 2 bird's-eye chilies, finely chopped
- 1 butternut squash, peeled and chopped
- 100 ml 3½ fl. oz vegetable stock broth
- 1 tablespoon olive oil

- Juice of 1 orange

- Juice of 1 lime

- 2 teaspoons honey

Directions:

- Warm the oil into a pan and add in the red onions, squash chunks, chilies, garlic, ginger and honey. Cook for 3 minutes.
- Squeeze in the lime and orange juice. Pour in the stock broth, orange and lime juice and cook for 15 minutes until tender.

Nutrition:

- Calories: 214

- Total Fat: 6 g

- Cholesterol: 60 mg

- Total Carbohydrates: 24 g

- Protein: 18 g

Lightning Source UK Ltd.
Milton Keynes UK
UKHW020654310521
384668UK00001B/172